Getting Started With the HomePod Mini

A RIDICULOUSLY SIMPLE GUIDE TO THE HOMEPOD MINI

Scott La Counte

ANAHEIM, CALIFORNIA

www.RidiculouslySimpleBooks.com

Table of Contents

***Disclaimer**: Please note, while every effort has been made to ensure accuracy, this book is not endorsed by Apple, Inc. and should be considered unofficial.*

Introduction

When the HomePod launched in 2018, critics praised its sound quality while also questioning how it would ever compete in the competitive smart speaker market. Critics' speculation was mostly correct for several years; the price of the stunning sounding speaker was too great for most consumers.

Things changed in 2020. Apple had spent years perfecting the HomePod and was ready to power their knowledge into something smaller and cheaper: the HomePod mini.

The HomePod mini lacks the multiple speakers of its larger companion but still offers a robust, room-filling sound. Unlike many budget smart speakers, the HomePod mini is more than a cheap stocking stuffer that gets passed around like gadget fruitcake; it is proof that Apple is ready to disrupt the industry and become a smart speaker leader.

This book will guide you through how to get the most of Apple's mighty mini speaker.

[1]

SETTING THINGS UP

This chapter will cover:

- HomePod vs other smart speakers
- Unboxing
- Setting things up

HOMEPOD VS. HOMEPOD MINI

The original HomePod is three times the price of the HomePod mini—that much is obvious. It's also bigger. You can see a side-by-side comparison in the images below.

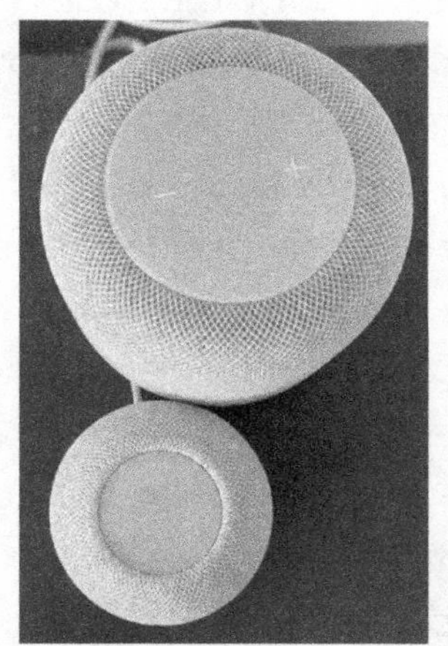

But what about some of the things that aren't quite as obvious? The original HomePod is several years older but still sounds better. That's because it has more speakers inside. The HomePod mini has one full-range driver; the original HomePod has one woofer and seven tweeters. There's also room sensing technology in the original HomePod that gives it the same superior sound no matter how you position it.

The original HomePod has six microphones (vs. the mini's four); that means the original will pick up voice commands much easier, but that's probably not going to be a big problem. The mini works better as a desk or nightstand speaker, where the original HomePod is more for a large room where you might be further away when you make a voice command.

Both have a fabric mesh covering the unit, which helps the sound and also makes it look and feel very high-end. While the top, touch portion of each device seems to be built of the same material, the mini feels, in my opinion, less responsive; chances are, however, you won't use it that often, as the device functions best using voice commands.

Both devices have a power cord that is physically attached to the unit; this makes it a little hard to feed the cable in tight places; the end of the original HomePod is a three-prong plug; the end of the mini is USB-C and plugs into an included adaptor.

HomePod Mini vs. Other Smart Speakers

There are a lot of smart speakers out there, and which is better can get pretty subjective. Personally, I think the sound quality of the HomePod mini beats others that are similarly priced; but others are going to disagree.

The one thing to consider in terms of the competition is how long Apple has been doing this; it's still relatively new to this space. If you have already used competing smart speakers, then you might find it lacks features that you really love. Spotify, for example, does not work (as of this writing); it probably will come soon. As interest in the HomePod mini builds, more and more developers will support it. The same is true for supported Smart Home devices; several devices are available for HomePod, but not nearly as many as other smart speakers.

That said, the HomePod mini is ideal for some invested in the Apple ecosystem. If you have an Apple home (you have an Apple TV connected to your TV, an iPad for couch browsing, a MacBook for work, an Apple Watch for fitness, and an iPhone for communication), then you'll love this little speaker because it works well with all of them.

Unboxing

The unboxing is like anything Apple makes: simple.

Simple as the unboxing is, I will point out a few things. Starting with the top, this is the only interactive part of the HomePod. You'll find no other controls—I'll cover the controls later, but they are ridiculously simple!

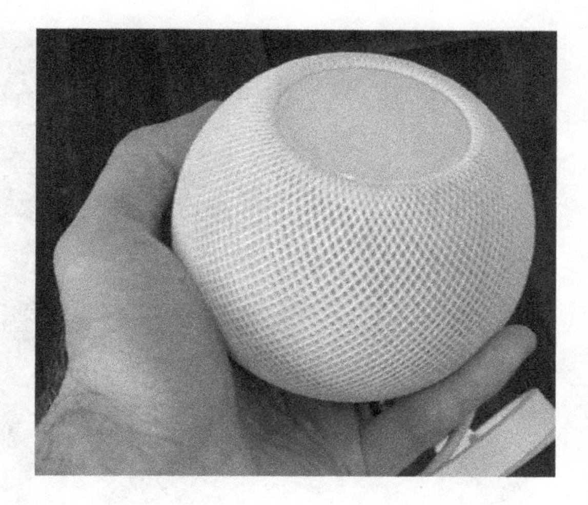

The back of the unit is the plug, which is physically attached to the unit—which means you can't remove it. There's also no other output/inputs—so you can connect this to something like a record player that doesn't have wi-fi. This is purely a Bluetooth device.

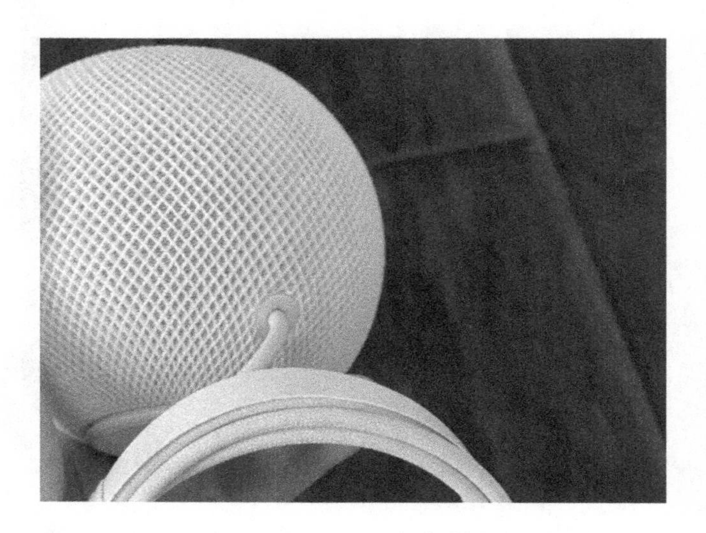

The HomePod connects to a USB-C adaptor. It's the same one that the iPhone uses. It's becoming standard on devices. Even the beefier MacBook computers use USB-C to charge. Most new gadgets have moved (or are moving) to USB-C for charging, which makes it much more universal with other things you will buy in the future.

SETTING THINGS UP

So there's only a handful of buttons; no output/inputs—how on earth do you connect this thing? It's simple! Plug the mini in, then grab the iPhone with the account you want to be associated with it, and tap the HomePod. That's going to bring up a little Set Up widget on your iPhone.

Once you begin the Set Up, it will ask you what room it's in. Why? Because if you have multiple speakers you can ask it to broadcast to specific rooms. So you want to make sure it's easy to remember.

The next question is optional; it will ask if it can recognize your voice. Why? So if you say something like "Play my playlist" it will know who is asking and make more personalized recommendations.

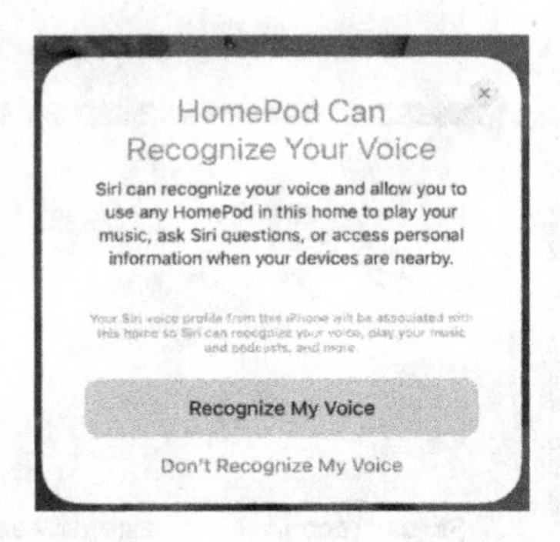

You can also have your HomePod make personal requests based on what's on your iPhone.

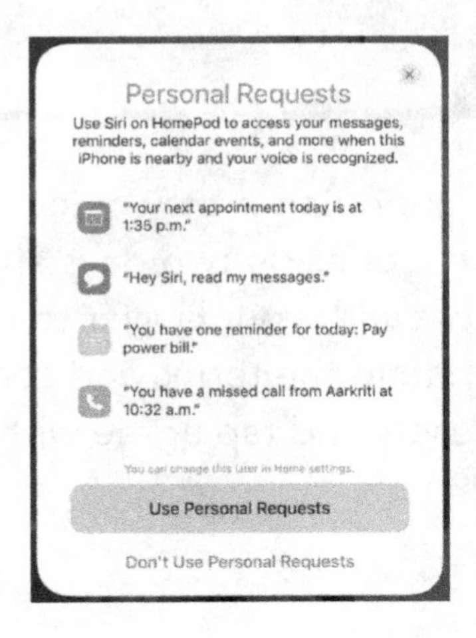

But what if you want other people to be able to get their own music when it's associated with your account? That's what the next screen tells you; once the set up is complete, you'll be able to add them.

Things are going pretty quick and smooth, right? Next, set aside two days and set up an appointment with your lawyer to make sure you fully understand the terms and conditions. Or be like most users and tap agree without reading them!

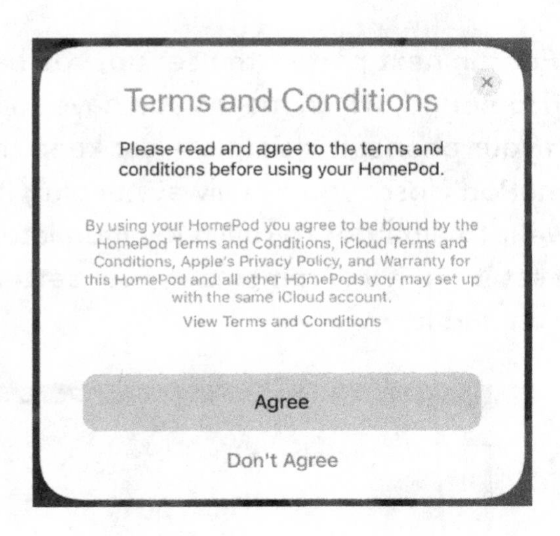

To make your life easier, you don't have to set up wi-fi or iCloud on your HomePod—it's transferred from your iPhone.

For the next part of the set up, you have to pair the HomePod, which means you have to scan it with your phone. It's simple—just keep the HomePod close; you can always unplug it and move it to a harder to reach location later. Once you set it up, it will remember your settings even if you unplug it.

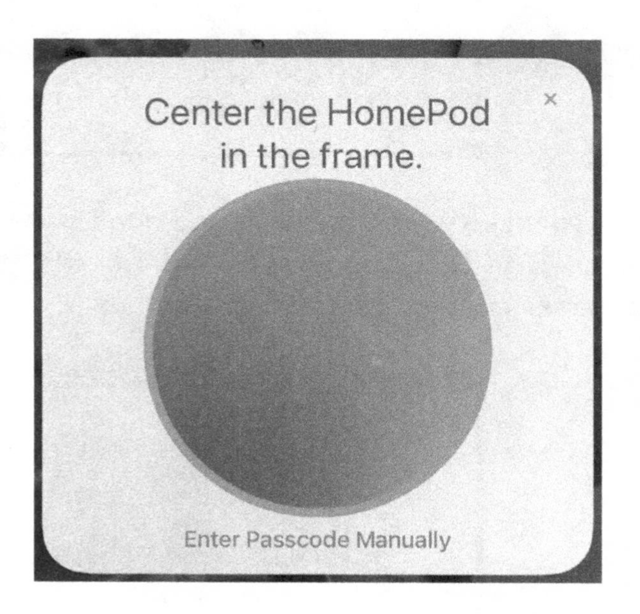

It's normal to see the set up spinner going for several seconds. You won't have to do anything during the process if you want to step away for a moment.

Once it's done setting up, it's going to have you ask Siri a question. Just repeat out loud what it says on your screen and wait for the HomePod mini to reply.

After you do this, it will give you a few suggested commands, and you are done. You are ready to use your HomePod mini, so go ahead and try asking it to do something—my personal favorite is "Hey Siri, tell me a joke." It knows where you live, so you can also ask for the weather in your location.

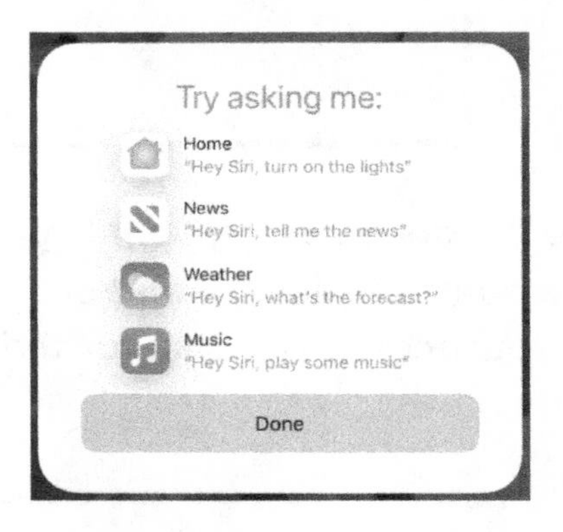

You'll know your mini is working when you see it lighting up.

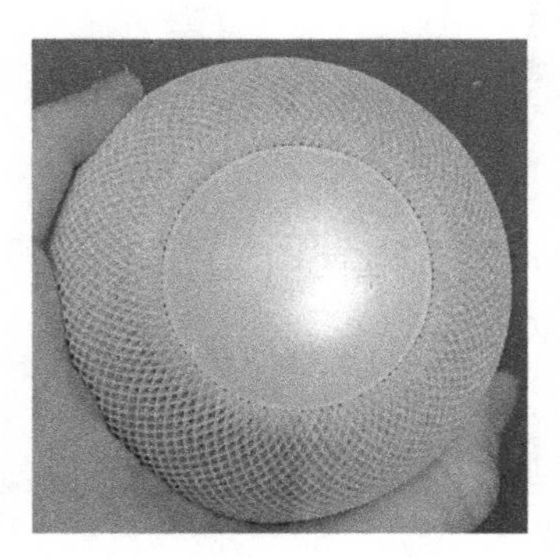

[2]
THE BASICS

This chapter will cover:

- Using intercom
- Pairing HomePod's
- AirPlay

Okay, so we have it set up—how do we actually use this thing?! The top of the HomePod mini has the only physical controls. There's a volume up and down.

Is that really all you can do? Kind of. Sort of. No.

If you've used AirPods, you might be familiar with the idea of tapping to get it to do certain things. That's similar to how HomePod works. There are six basic tap gestures:

- Tap - Play/pause
- Double-tap - Skip to next track
- Triple-tap - Skip back to the previous track
- Touch and hold - Summon Siri
- Tap or hold + - Volume up
- Tap or hold – - Volume down

If you want the top touch to be more or less sensitive to touch, then go to the Home app, tap HomePod, then Details, next Accessibility, and finally Touch Accommodations.

What about the power button? There is no power button! It's always on. The only way to turn it off is to unplug it.

What about playing music and Podcasts? That's how most of us will probably use the speaker, right? I'll go into this in more detail later, but telling Siri what to play (e.g. "Hey, Siri: play Queen's Greatest Hits") is one way. One very cool trick, however, is transferring a song from your iPhone (note: make sure you are on the same network).

What I mean is when you are playing a Podcast or song on your iPhone; walk to your HomePod and tap it to the top of the mini; it will stop playing on your phone and transfer it to your HomePod mini.

This works in reverse as well. Tap your iPhone to the HomePod mini while it's playing a song or Podcast, and it will transfer back to your device.

Using the Intercom

When the HomePod mini was revealed, one of the big features they promoted was the Intercom. Intercom can be used with just one HomePod, but it really shines with several. Intercom is exactly what it sounds like: it turns your HomePod into an intercom! So, for example, you could tell HomePod to announce that dinner is ready and every room with a HomePod will get the message. You no longer have to yell at everyone to come to dinner—HomePod does it for you!

Intercom works on both the mini and original HomePod, but to use it on your iPhone, iPad or Apple Watch, you may need to update the OS (on the device go to the Settings app, then General > Software Update). You need to have iOS 14.2 or later on your iPhone, iPadOS 14.2 if you are using iPad, and watchOS 7.2 if you want it on Apple Watch.

If you have multiple HomePods you could technically tell one HomePod to announce something to another. If you want to do this from an iPhone, iPad, or Apple Watch, however, then just say "Hey Siri" then say "Intercom [message here]". What's cool about this, is you can do it when you are outside your home. For example, you could be heading home from work and say, "Hey Sir, intercom 'I'm on my way home.'" Intercom is the command that's easiest to remember, but you can also say, "Hey, Siri: announce [message here]", "Hey, Siri: ask / tell everyone [message here]". You can also intercom a specific HomePod, so you can say, for example, "Hey, Siri: Intercom Office HomePod, are you almost done with work?"

You can also reply to an intercom message by saying "Hey, Siri: reply (or announce back) [message here]". If that message was sent to every HomePod in the house, then that reply also goes to every HomePod; but if it was sent to only that specific HomePod, then the reply goes to where it originated from.

Turning Intercom Off

I'm a big fan of Intercom. Usually. Sure it's nice in most settings, but there might be times when you don't want a specific HomePod to announce something. If you want to disable it in some situations, then go to the Home app (I'll cover this more throughout the book—it's where you make most of your HomePod changes).

Once the app is open, tap the little Home icon in the upper left corner, then select the HomePod you want to control. In the below example, there are two HomePods: Living Room and Office; I'm going to make changes to the Office.

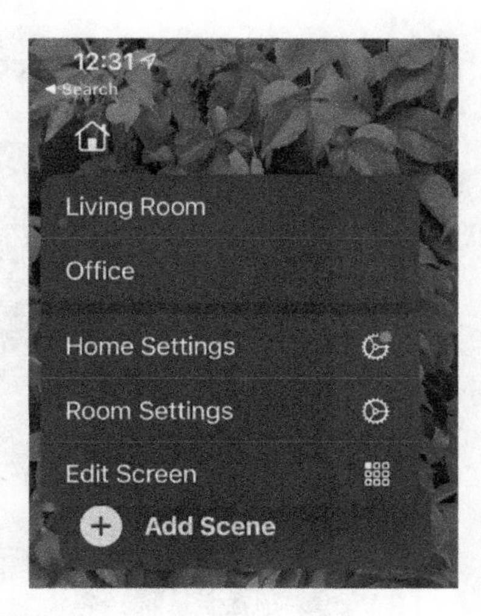

Once it's selected, you should see a checkbox next to it; if you see that, then tap Home Settings.

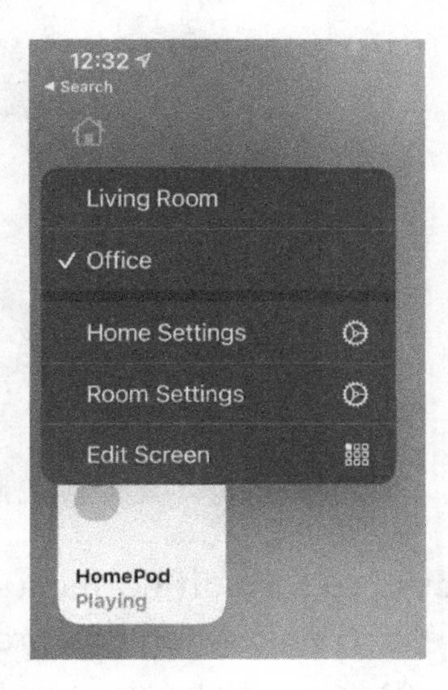

Tap the option that says "Intercom."

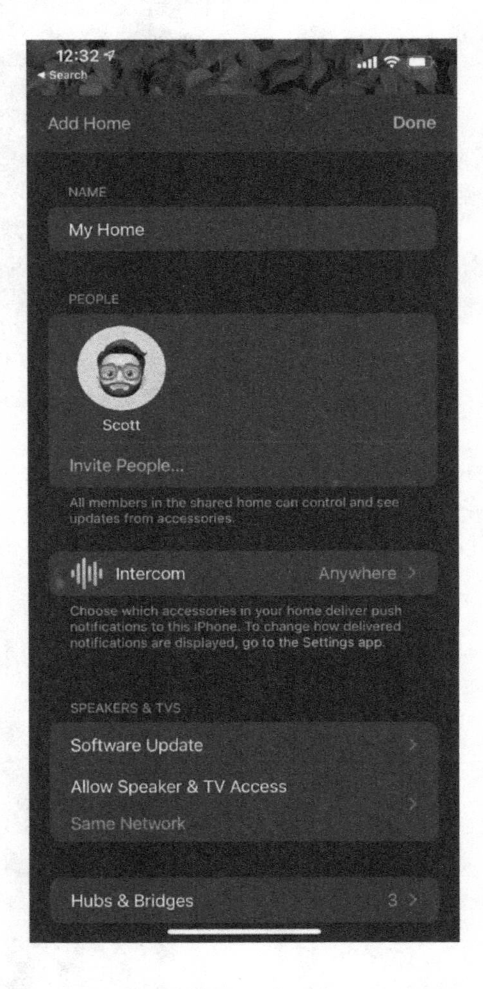

Tap Never to turn off notifications. You can also toggle it to only when you are home or Anywhere. At the very bottom of this screen,

there's an on / off toggle to turn off the feature entirely, so no one can intercom your HomePod. You can also turn off intercom notifications from specific people.

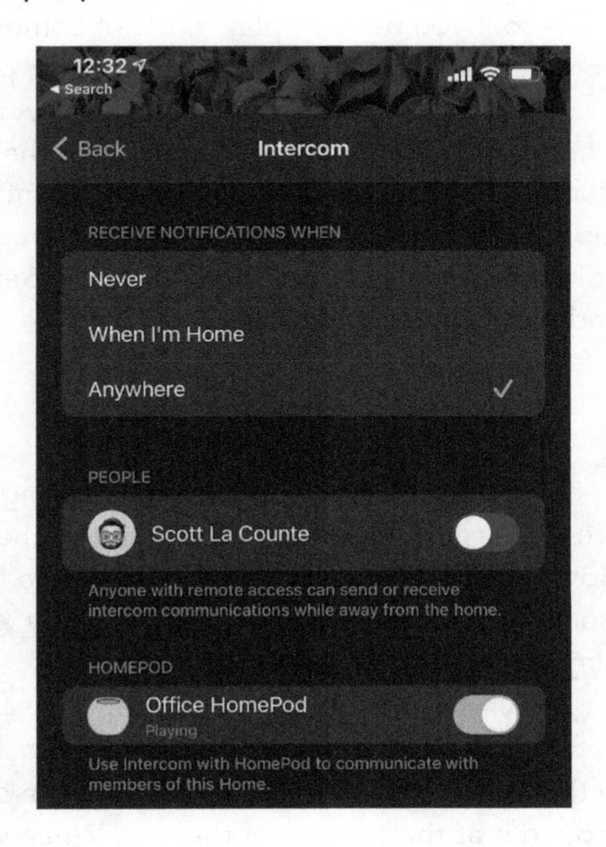

Pairing HomePod Mini With Another mini

One cool feature with themini is you can pair it with other minis to create a stereo sound (note:

you can pair the original HomePod with another original HomePod, or a mini with another mini, but you cannot pair an original HomePod with a mini.)

In stereo mode, two HomePods basically act as one—so if you tell it to play music, it comes out of both at the same time like a stereo music player.

To set it up, go to the Home app on your iPhone or iPad. You should see both of the HomePod minis; tap and hold one of them, then tap Create Stereo Pair. To unpair them, tap and hold the HomePod pair, then tap Audio Settings and follow the instructions.

AirPlay to the HomePod

Speaking a "play" command or tapping the mini are the easiest ways to stream music to the HomePod, but you can also AirPlay to the HomePod. AirPlay is streaming wirelessly what's playing on your device to the HomePod.

To AirPlay, make sure you are on the same network, then find the AirPlay button. For example, in the Music app, it's the triangle with the circles around it at the bottom of the app. When you tap this, it will show you all the possible places you can play it.

You will also find the AirPlay button when you access your Control Panel from the iPhone or iPad. It's in the upper right corner of the Now Playing section.

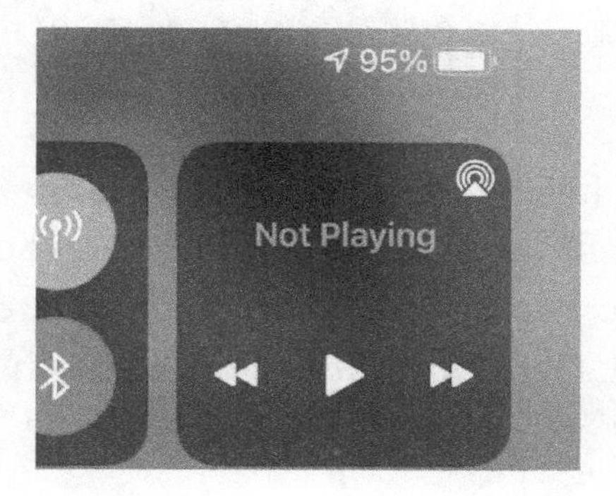

Similar to the Music AirPlay, it will give you a list of where you can stream it.

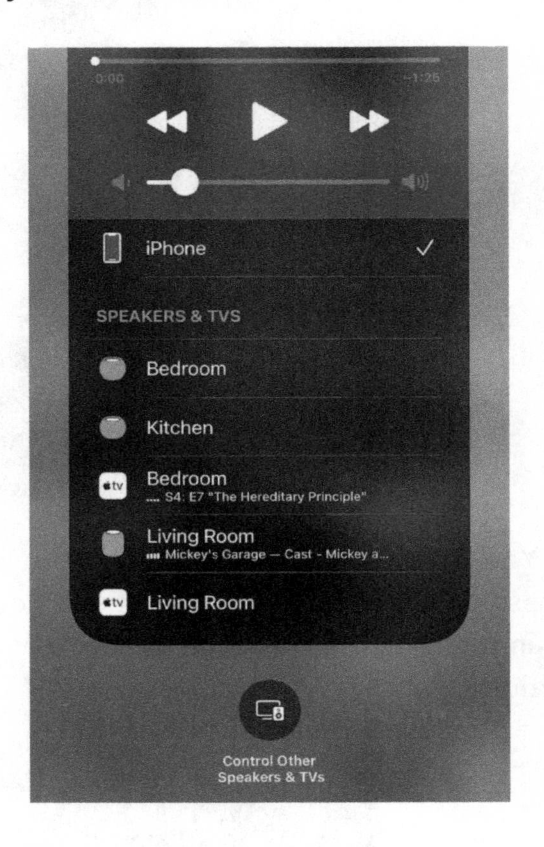

AirPlay is found on most popular apps. In YouTube, for example, it's on the top of videos (the rectangular box with the half circles in the corner). Clicking that will give you the option to AirPlay.

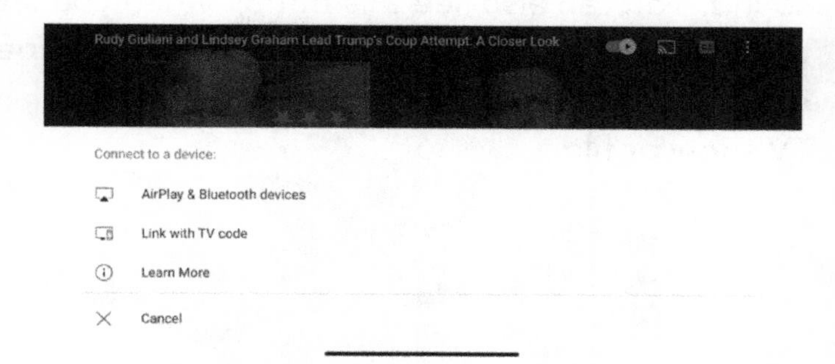

From there, the AirPlay menu will pop up and you can select the device you want to stream to.

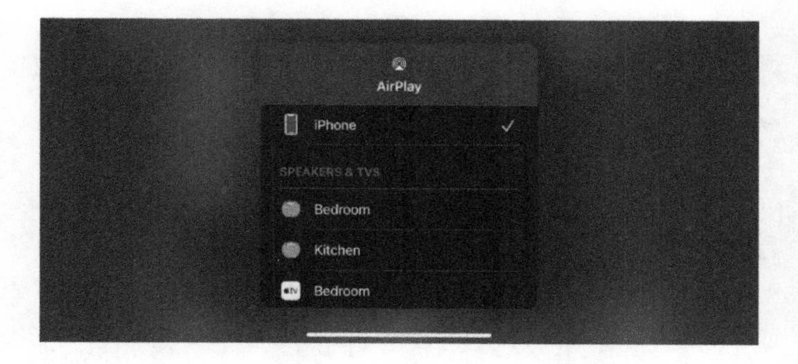

Finally, if you have an Apple TV, you can AirPlay Apple TV to your HomePod to essentially let them work as a stereo speaker. Unless you have multiple speakers, you probably won't be very happy with the sound. This option really shines when you are pairing the Apple TV with the original HomePod. To do this, go into the Apple TV settings, then find the audio settings and select the HomePod mini for sound. You can also see this option when you are watching something on Apple TV, and you swipe down; go to the audio options for that particular TV show or film.

[3]

HEY, SIRI!

This chapter will cover:

- Siri basics
- Siri commands
- Siri shortcuts

By now, you probably know all about Siri and how she can remind you of things.

Siri works the same as always on HomePod.

A lot of people, however, probably don't use Siri to the best of her potential. They know how to say "Hey, Siri: what's the weather," but they might be a little rusty on things like Siri shortcuts and automation. So let's learn just a little more about Siri here.

The first thing you should do is to introduce Siri to your family. Siri is pretty smart, and she wants to meet your family. To introduce her to your family say: "Hey, Siri" and "Brian is my brother" or "Susan is my boss." Once you confirm the relationship you can now say things like: "Call my brother" or "Email my boss."

Siri is also location-based. What does that mean? It means that instead of saying, "Remind me to call wife at 5PM" you can say, "Remind me when I leave work to call wife," and as soon as you step out of the office you will receive a reminder. Siri can be a bit frustrating at first, but it's one of the phone's most powerful apps, so give it a chance!

Everyone hates to deal with waiting. There's nothing worse than being hungry and having to wait an hour for a table. Siri does her best to make your life easier by making reservations for you. For this to work, you'll need a free app called "OpenTable" (you'll also need a free account), which is in the Apple App Store. This app makes its money from restaurants paying it, so don't worry about having to pay to use it. Once it's installed, you will simply activate Siri (press the Home button until it turns on) and say, "Siri, make me a reservation at the Olive Garden," (or wherever you want to eat). Note that not all restaurants participate in OpenTable, but hundreds (if not thousands) do, and it's growing monthly, so if it's not there, it probably will be soon.

Siri is ever-evolving. Apple has taught her everything she needs to know about sports. Go ahead, try it! Say something like: "Hey, Siri: What's the score in the Kings game" or: "Who leads the league in home runs?"

Siri has also gotten a little wiser in movies. You can say, "Hey, Siri: Movies directed by Peter Jackson" and it will give you a list and let you see a synopsis, the review rating from Rotten Tomatoes, and in some cases even a trailer or an option to buy the movie. You can also say, "Movie showtimes" and nearby movies that are playing will appear.

iOS also lets you add shortcuts to Siri; you can see this in Settings > Siri & Search > Short cuts.

Basic Siri Commands

General Knowledge - Siri has a very encyclopedic knowledge-base—partially because Siri gets a lot of her information from Wikipedia! You can ask hundreds of thousands of general questions and she'll tell you the answer. Things like "Hey Siri, who is the President of France?", "Hey Siri, what does the word Joyful mean", or "Hey Siri, who was Pocahontas?"

Weather - Because Siri knows your location, you can say "Hey Siri, what's the weather?" And it will immediately give you a forecast for your current location. You can also ask it about weather in the future, "Hey Siri, what's the weather this weekend?" or weather in other locations, "Hey Siri, what's the weather in Tokyo?"

Alarms and Timers - Siri is a clock, alarm and timer all rolled into one. It can tell you the time anywhere in the world, and can also set an alarm or timer. So, you can say, "Hey Siri, wake me up at 4:00 am" (and say, "Hey Siri, snooze" when you realize what 4:00 am feels like!), or "Hey Siri, set a 10-minute timer." You can set multiple alarms and timers if needed.

Sports - Sports fans will love Siri's sports knowledge. It's up-to-date, so you can say "Hey Siri, what's the score in the Clippers game" or ask it about the future, "Hey Siri, who do the Angels play next?" Siri also loves sports trivia. Go ahead, ask her for facts like, "Hey Siri, who is the top home run hitter of all time?"

Stocks - Siri isn't just up-to-date with Sports; it's up-to-date with stocks too. Ask about the exchange, "Hey Siri, where's the NASDAQ at?" or ask about a particular stock.

Calculator - There's no need to crunch numbers yourself anymore. Let Siri do it for you! It can do calculations like "Hey Siri, what's the square root of 324?" It can also do conversions, "Hey Siri, how many feet are in a mile?" Or tell you about currency, "Hey Siri, convert one dollar to Euro."

Translations - Siri is bilingual. It can translate simple phrases or words into French, German, Italian, Spanish, and Mandarin Chinese. Try it by saying something like, "Hey Siri, translate 'where is the subway' into Spanish."

Hey, Siri: Be My Assistant

Siri can also work as your personal assistant. You can ask your HomePod to send a message, make phone calls (yes, you can talk to someone on your HomePod mini), or read what's on your calendar. There's usually no exact way to ask Siri something—no one specific command that is; Siri does a good job interpreting what you are trying to ask. So just ask her to do something (e.g. Hey, Siri: send a text to my sister) and see what happens.

In the case of phone calls, the HomePod is basically being used as a speakerphone for your connected phone.

Did you already answer a call on your phone? No problem! Just tap the HomePod mini with your phone and it will be transferred to your HomePod mini!

Siri Commands

The bread and button of the HomePod is Siri. Controlling the HomePod is really all about controlling Siri. So, let's get a crash course in some of the things Siri can do.

Music

The HomePod is, unsurprisingly, built for Apple Music—the music subscription service Apple launched about two years ago. Apple offers a free trial subscription to it. You can also stream other music using AirPlay, but to really get the most out of the HomePod, Apple Music is the way to go.

Apple Music is pretty smart. It takes note of what you are listening to and starts getting a feel for your taste. So, saying "Hey Siri, play some music" will make the HomePod play songs that it thinks you will like. When you are listening to music, you can also say "Hey Siri, I like this" so Siri will make a note to play it again—or songs similar.

Siri can also be used as a DJ. Let's say you're throwing an 80s party. Say "Hey Siri, play 1980s dance music" and an 80s playlist will be delivered. You can also throw out a mood, "Hey Siri, play romantic music."

Playing a song is as simple as saying, "Hey Siri, play me NAME OF SONG," but many songs have more than one version. Say "Hey Siri, play the other version" and you'll immediately get the next song. Like what you're hearing? Say, "Hey Siri, add this to my library."

Beats 1 is the main listening station of Apple Music. It plays news, interviews, and more from studios in Los Angeles, New York and London. If you want to hear it on your HomePod, just say, "Hey Siri, play Beats 1."

News

News is one of the main features of any smart speaker. This feature basically pulls in top news from different stations (i.e. CNN, Fox News, NPR, etc.); these feeds last just a few minutes each and normally change throughout the day. To hear the news, just say "Hey Siri, tell me the news today" and Siri will start replaying different broadcast. You can skip the broadcast by saying "Hey Siri, skip" or you can go right to the one you want, "Hey Siri, switch to NPR news." You can also tell Siri to only bring back specific topic news like sports or business by saying, "Hey Siri, tell me the latest business news."

Messages, Reminders and Notes

To set up Messages, Reminders, and Notes, your iOS device (iPad or iPhone) needs to be on the same Wi-Fi network, and your iPhone or iPad needs to be the one you share your location from using Find My Friends. Why? Because your HomePod is essentially using your phone or tablet to make these requests. It's almost like it's tethered to it. To get started, go to Settings on your phone, tap the top where it shows your name, then iCloud > Share My Location > From > This Device. Chances are it's already selected.

Send a Message. To send a message say, "Hey Siri, send a message to INSERT NAME HERE." Siri will ask for the message, and you can just dictate it.

Read a Message(s). Say "Hey Siri, read messages" to hear your unread messages. You can also say whose message you want to hear. For instance, "Hey Siri, read me message from wife.

Reminders. Reminders are pretty straightforward. Just say, "Hey Siri, remind me in X minutes to Y." You can also use this to make lists. "Hey Siri, put soda on my shopping list." Then you can later ask, "Hey Siri, what's on my shopping list?"

Notes. Notes work almost identically to Reminders. Just say "Hey Siri, add a note that says..."

Remember: this is public on your HomePod! So, anyone can ask Siri for your reminders, or can even send a message without you knowing! Understandably, you might want this feature turned off. If you want it off, go to the Home app, , tap your name, then turn off Personal Requests.

Siri Shortcuts

Siri Shortcuts is one of the most powerful apps on your phone. And probably the one most people never use. What is it?

Shortcuts might not be the best way to describe it. Automation does it more justice, in my opinion. It's a way to teach Siri how to automate the things you do often in life.

Let me give an example:

Let's say you have a playlist when you plug your phone into CarPlay. You always play it on shuffle. You stop it when you get to your location.

The old way of doing this was manual. The new way to do this is just to plug in the phone and let your phone do the rest.

Absolutely nothing for you to do.

Siri Shortcuts becomes easier in iOS because it's all built into the phone with a native pre-installed app.

What does HomePod have to do with this? You can also create Siri Shortcuts to do something like start playing music on your HomePod when you get home from work.

Shortcuts vs. Automation

When you first open the app, you'll see three menus on the bottom: shortcuts, automation, gallery. What's the difference?

Shortcuts are things you can actually add to your phone, sort of like apps—so you could have an icon representing your shortcut right on your Home screen. Automation is the actions your phone takes when something happens—you plug it into CarPlay, for example, the phone does X. Gallery is pre-made automation that you can add.

USING SHORTCUTS

To create a shortcut, go to the shortcut menu and tap Create Shortcut.

Next, select: Add Action.

From here, you define the shortcut. Do you want to have a shortcut whenever you want to play your workout playlist, for example? Tap Media. I'm going to create a shortcut to call my wife, so I don't have to go into the phone app to do it. Under suggestions, I'm selecting Call and Wife

The shortcut is created. From here I can tap the '+' button to create an additional action. For example, whenever I call her, get the current driving time so I can tell her how far I am from home.

If I tap the three dots, I can customize the shortcut.

Once I give it a name, I can add it to my Home screen with "Add to Home Screen." From here, if I tap on the small icon, I can choose a custom photo to assign to it.

Once you add it, it will appear on your Home screen.

The shortcut also appears in your Siri Shortcut app.

To remove it, long-press it. Then tap Delete.

Using Automation

Adding automation is similar to the method used for shortcuts. Select Automation from the Siri Shortcut menu. You have two options. Personal automation and Home automation. Personal is an automation that would be on your iOS device for you to use. Home automation would be something accessible to anyone in your home and is ideal for something like the HomePod.

Once you select Create, you'll see a series of suggestions. Select the ones you want and follow the steps.

To remove the automation, swipe over it and select Delete.

[4]

ADVANCED SETTINGS

This chapter will cover:

- Advantaged settings
- Securing your HomePod Mini

Turn off the HomePod. Did you try? If so you might be a bit stumped. There are no physical buttons on the HomePod; sure, you could unplug it, but that's really not great on the hardware. So, what do you do?

There's really one main reason someone would want to turn off the HomePod: to make it stop listening. You don't have to turn it off for that, however! Just say "Hey Siri, stop listening." You'll still be able to manually activate Siri by touching and holding the top of the HomePod and speaking. To turn listening back on, go to the Home app, tap the HomePod, then tap Details and change the listen for "Hey Siri."

Just like your phone uses your location to provide services like weather, local traffic and nearby businesses, your HomePod does too. If you don't want it to, go into your Home app, tap the HomePod, then details, and change the Location Services setting.

Reset HomePod. I'm sure you'll be using the HomePod for a long time...but no gadget stays with you forever. Eventually, you might want to give it away. Before you do, you'll need to reset the HomePod to make sure your information is no longer on it. It's quick and painless. Go into the Home app, tap HomePod, tap Details, then tap Remove Accessory.

Secure Your HomePod

The HomePod is pretty secure; no one can access it that doesn't know your wi-fi password; but you can restrict it even more. Go into the Home app on your iPhone or iPad, then select your HomePod in the upper left corner, and tap Home Settings; from Allow Speaker & TV Access, you can restrict who can access it and also require a password.

INDEX

W

About the Author

Scott La Counte is a librarian and writer. His first book, *Quiet, Please: Dispatches from a Public Librarian* (Da Capo 2008) was the editor's choice for the Chicago Tribune and a Discovery title for the Los Angeles Times; in 2011, he published the YA book The N00b Warriors, which became a #1 Amazon bestseller; his most recent book is *#OrganicJesus: Finding Your Way to an Unprocessed, GMO-Free Christianity* (Kregel 2016).

He has written dozens of best-selling how-to guides on tech products.

You can connect with him at ScottDouglas.org.